Scribble

Ruth Ohi

Scholastic Canada Ltd.
Toronto New York London Auckland Sydney
Mexico City New Delhi Hong Kong Buenos Aires

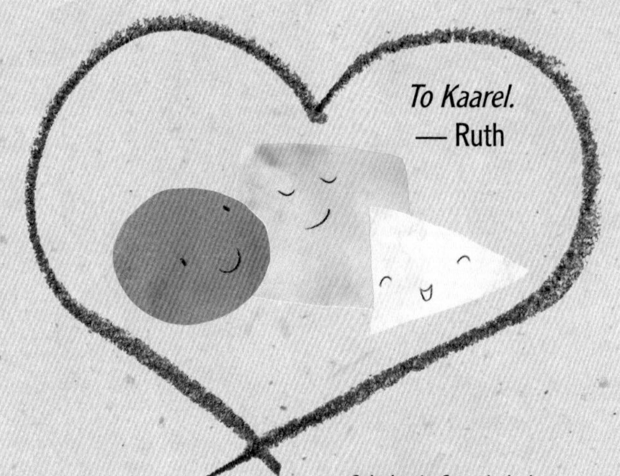

Scholastic Canada Ltd.
604 King Street West, Toronto, Ontario M5V 1E1, Canada

Scholastic Inc.
557 Broadway, New York, NY 10012, USA

Scholastic Australia Pty Limited
PO Box 579, Gosford, NSW 2250, Australia

Scholastic New Zealand Limited
Private Bag 94407, Botany, Manukau 2163, New Zealand

Scholastic Children's Books
Euston House, 24 Eversholt Street, London NW1 1DB, UK

www.scholastic.ca

The artwork was rendered primarily in watercolour, pencil crayon, pastel and found paper, then assembled digitally.

Library and Archives Canada Cataloguing in Publication
Ohi, Ruth, author, illustrator
Scribble / Ruth Ohi.
ISBN 978-1-4431-4666-1 (paperback)
I. Title.
PS8579.H47S37 2016a jC813'.6 C2015-905473-7

Author photo by Annie T.

9 8 7 6 5 4 Printed in Malaysia 108 20 21 22 23 24

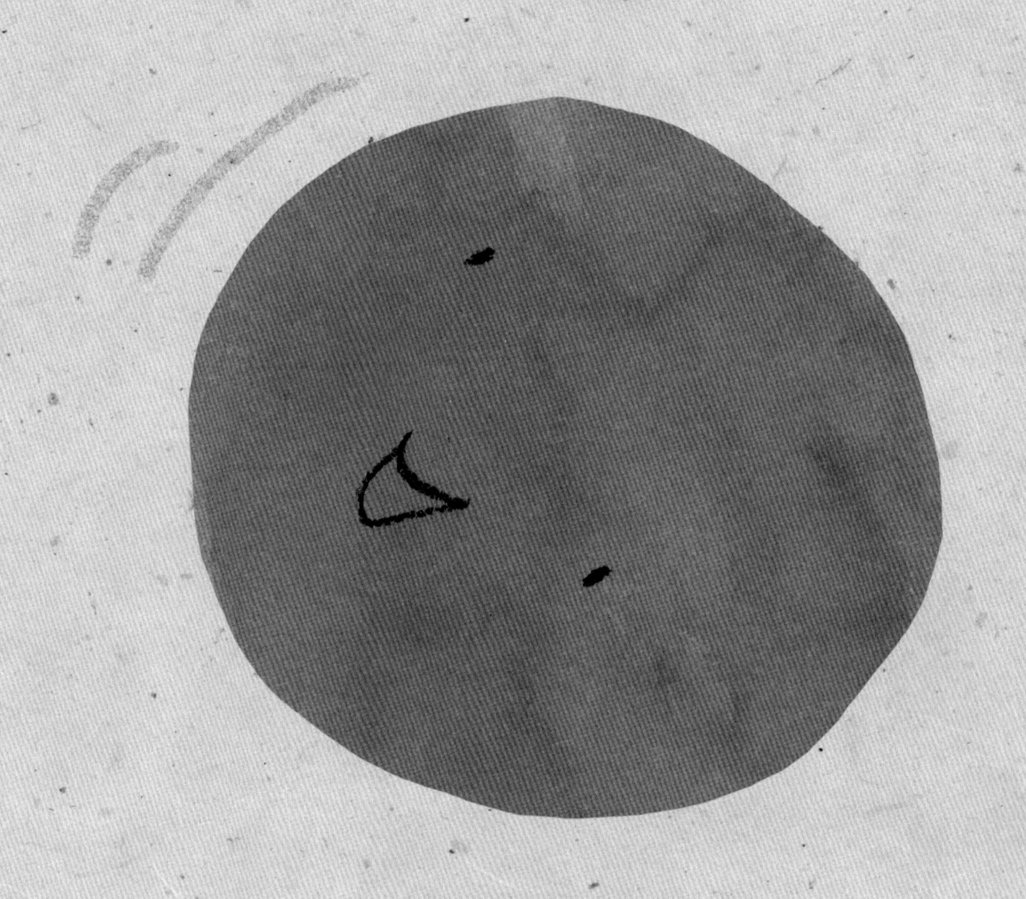

I like to roll, around and around!

I like to sit still.
I am solid and strong.

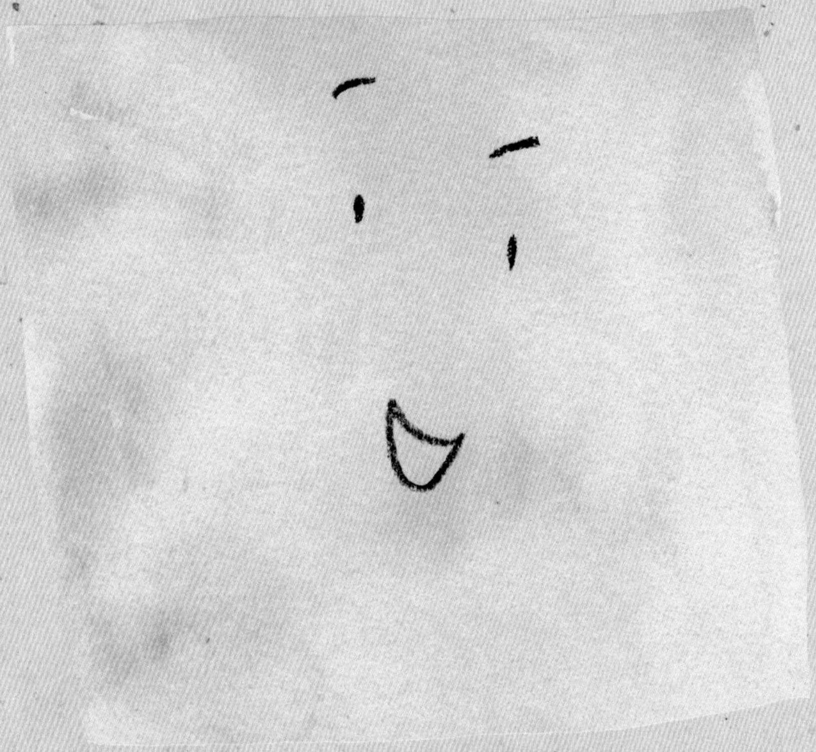

I have many points — all of them good ones.

Straight lines are best.

Follow me and you will
never get lost!

Za-Zoom!

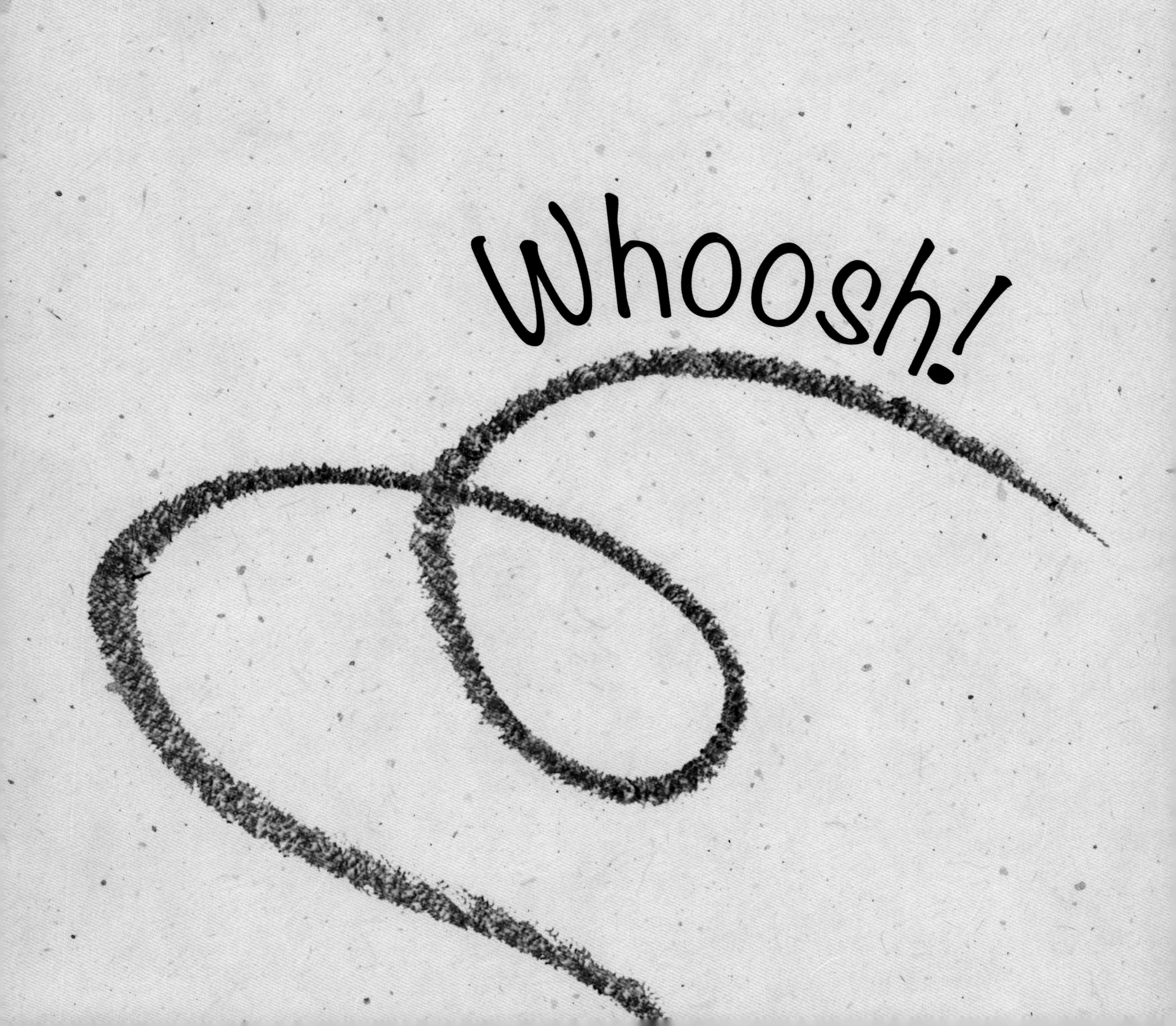
Whoosh!

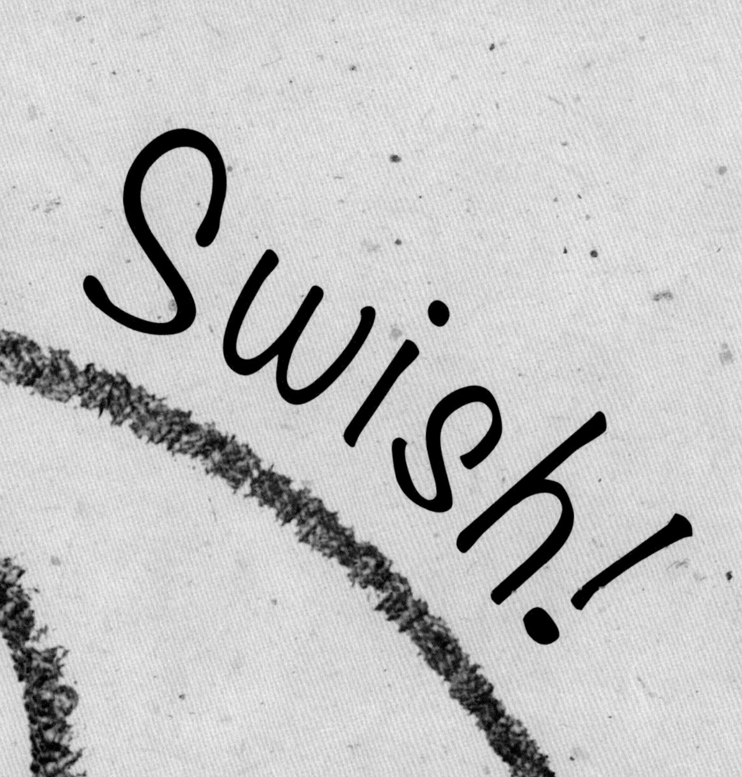

"Eek!" said Circle.

"Ack!" said Square.

Triangle trembled.

“What are you?” said Circle.

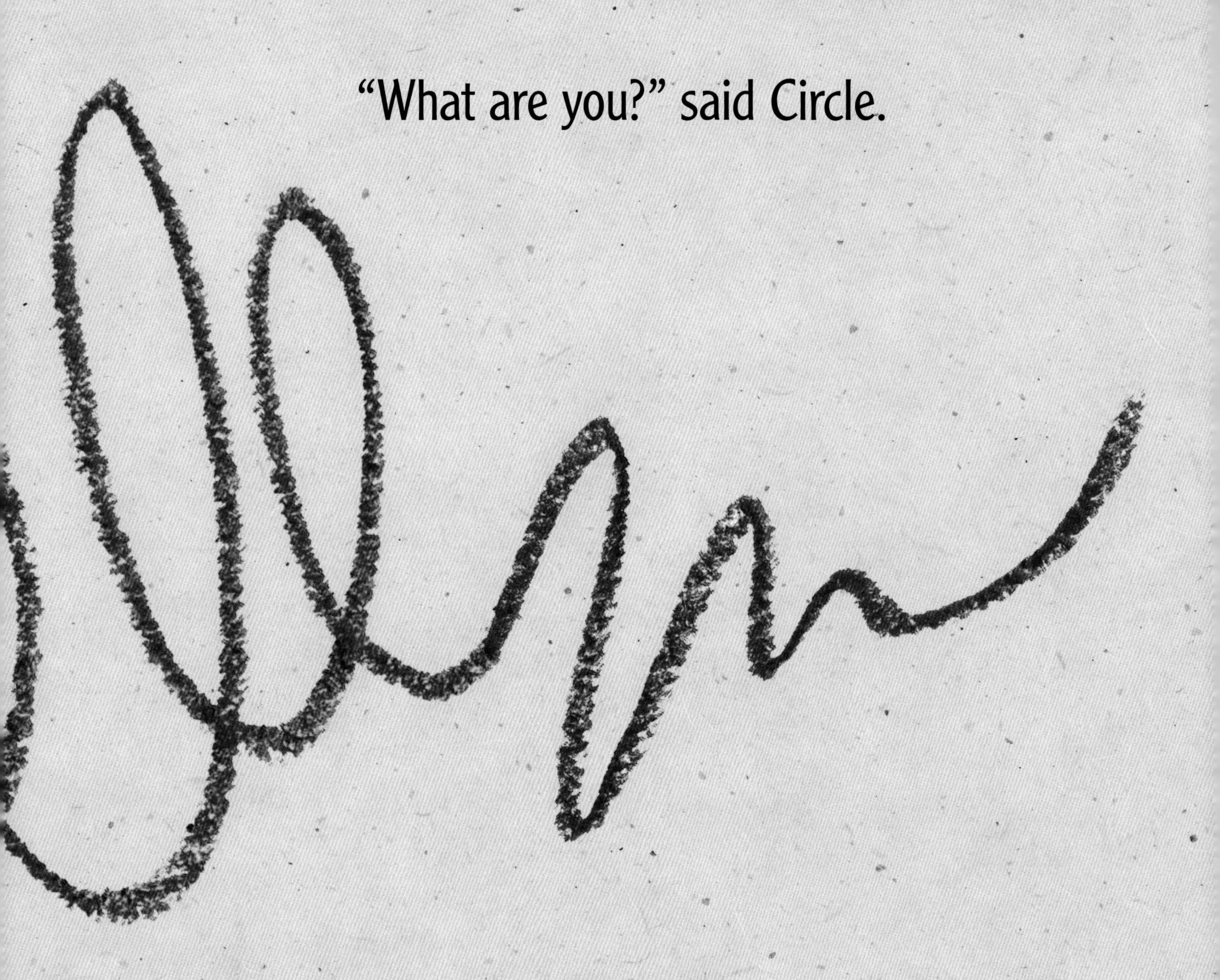

“I am Scribble,” said Scribble.

“That is not a shape,” said Square.

“Too many points,” said Triangle.

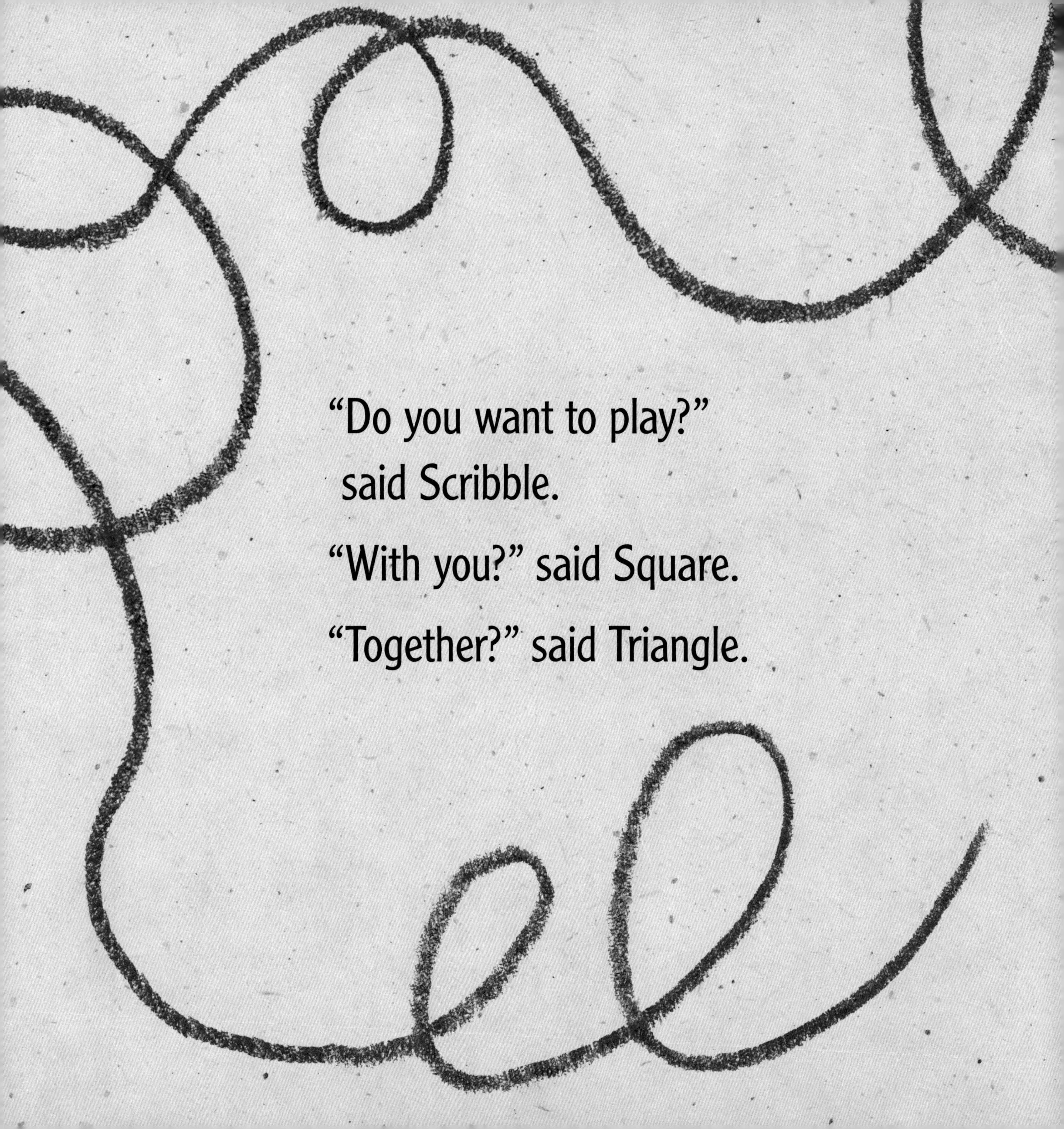

"Do you want to play?"
said Scribble.

"With you?" said Square.

"Together?" said Triangle.

“But why?” said Circle.

So Scribble swooped.

And Circle found out
that when scribbles waved . . .

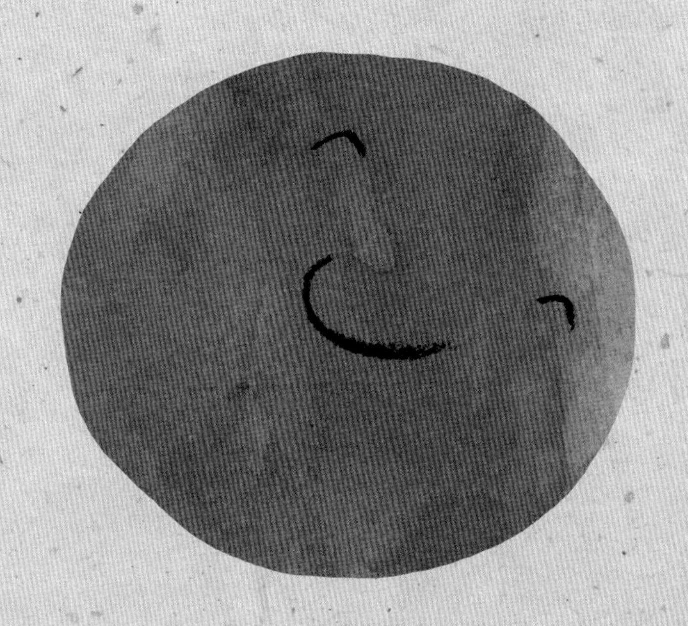

. . . circles shone bright.

When scribbles scurried,
circles could bounce up . . .

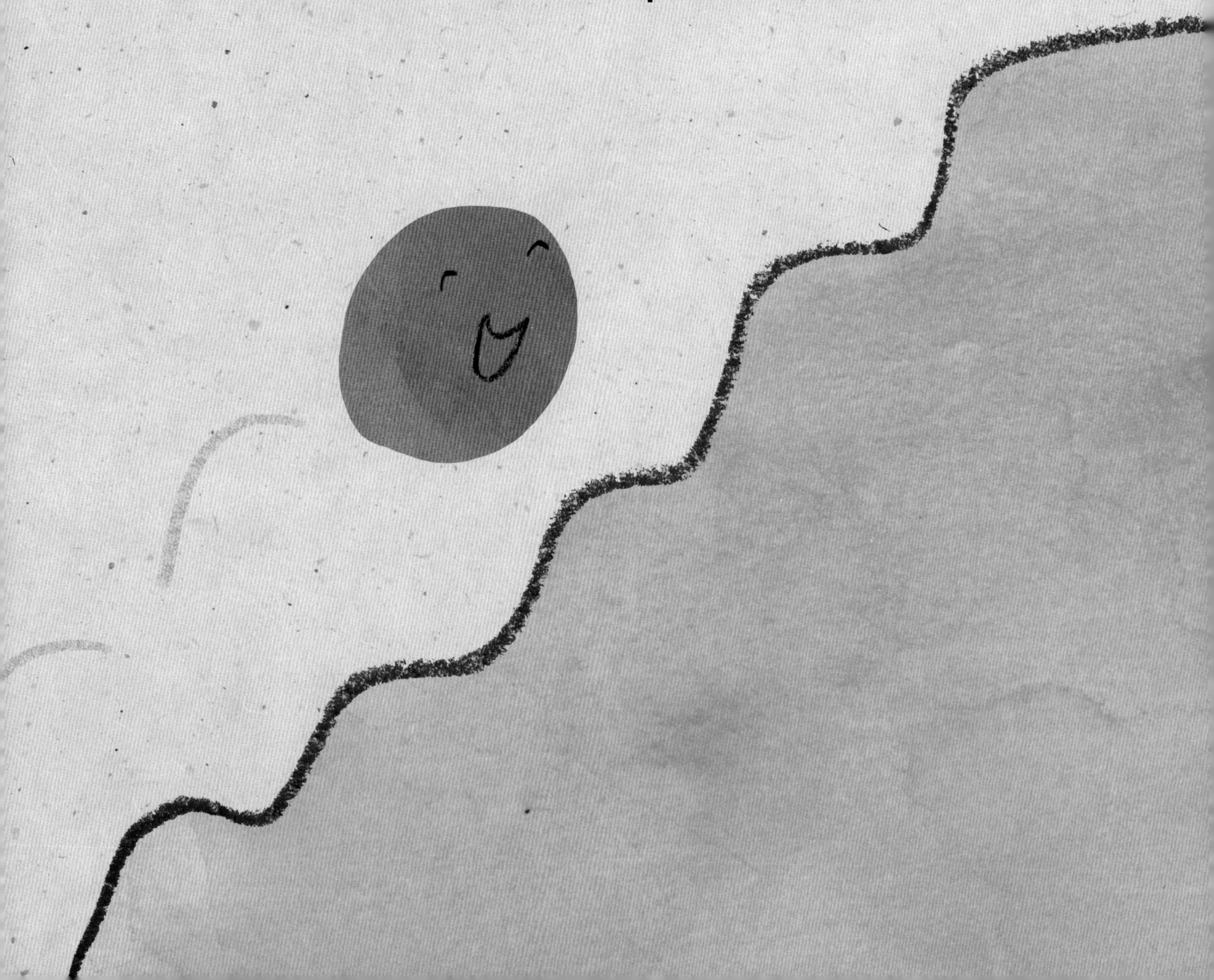

. . . and down.

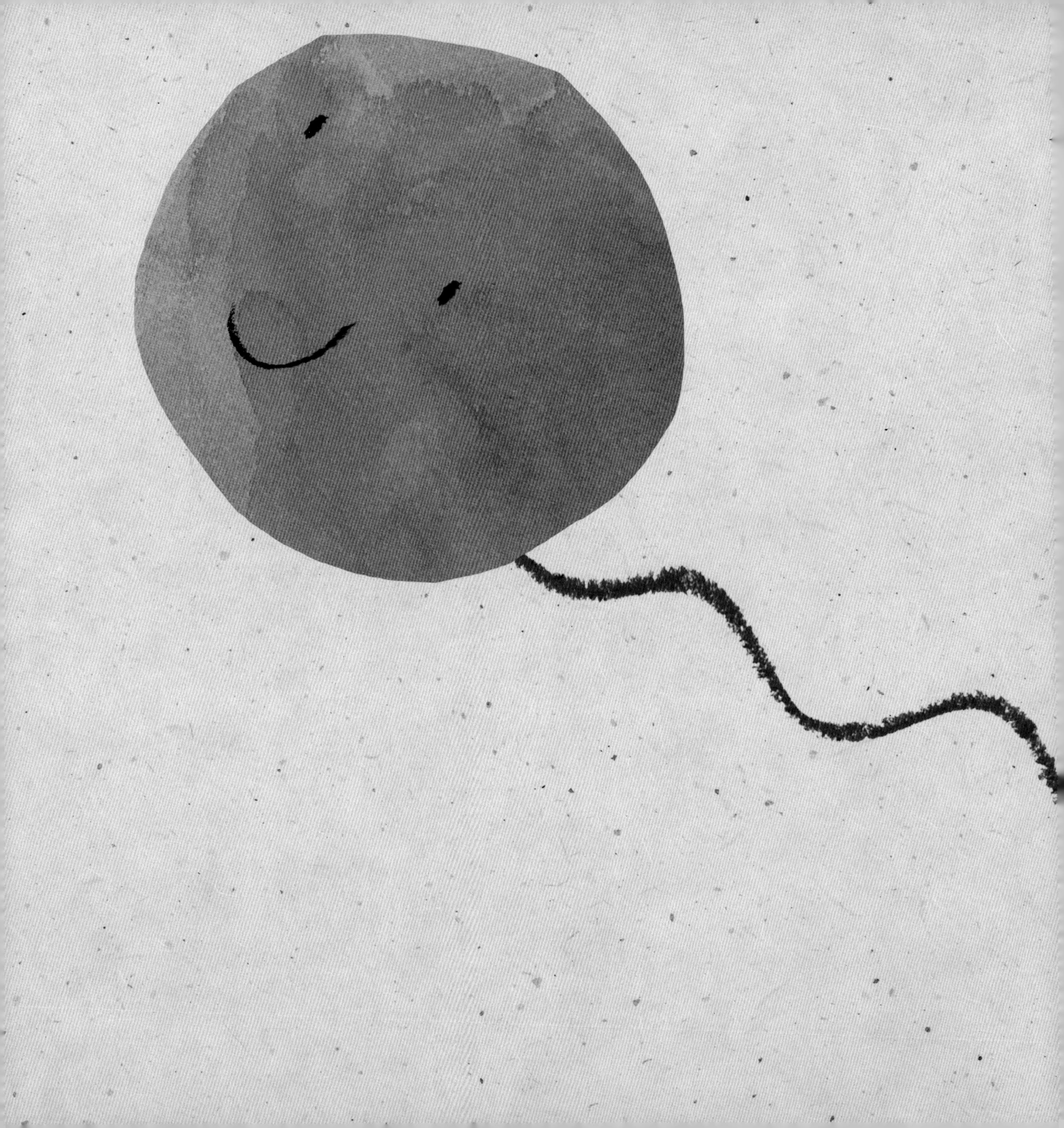

When Circle feared
she would float away,

Scribble held on tight.

When Scribble roared,

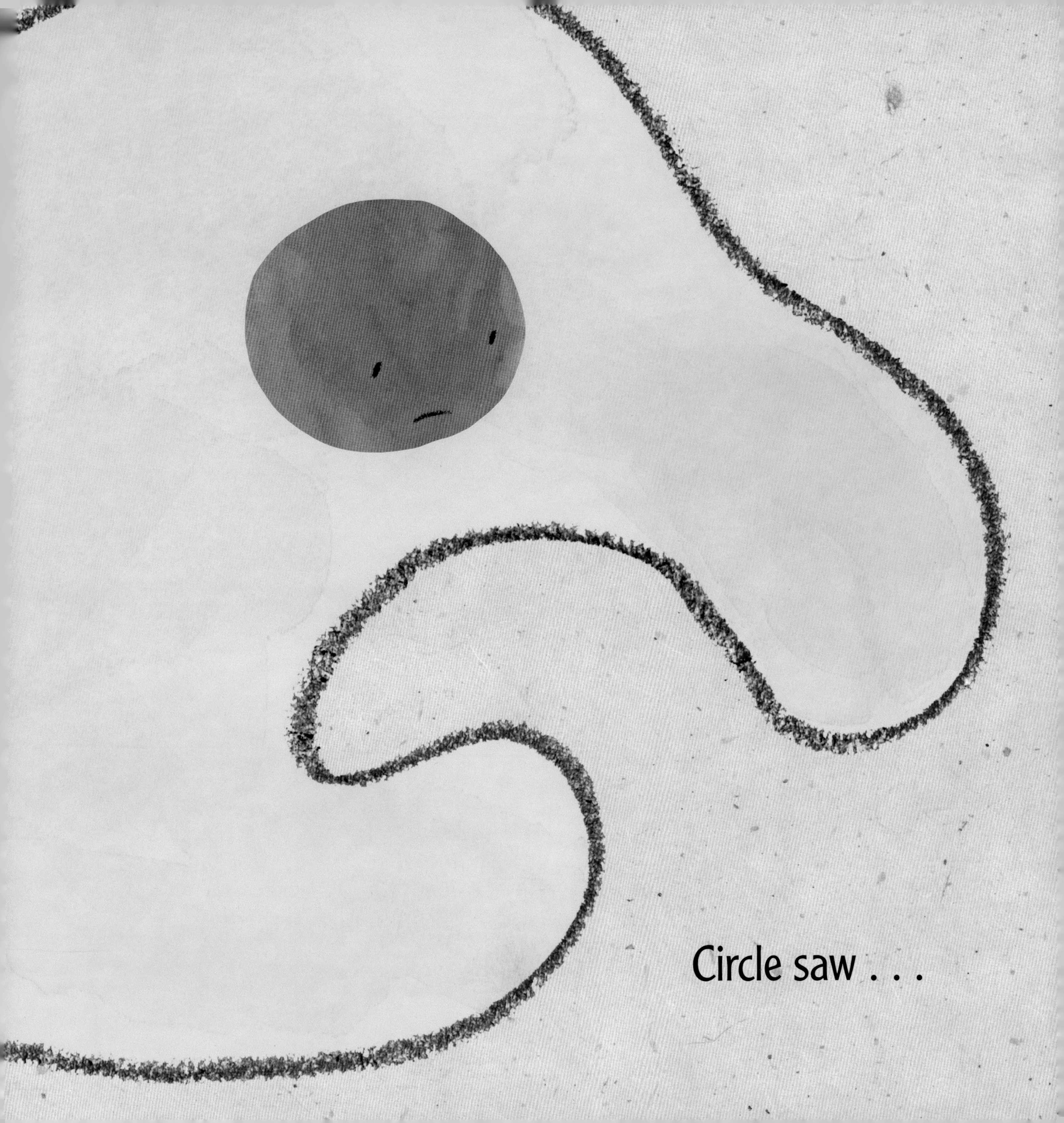

Circle saw . . .

And Circle saw Square and
Triangle wanting to join in.

“Come,” said Circle. “Come play.”

"Come, see what else you can be!"

"Hello. My name is Star!"